BOOK 3

FOUR STAR

SIGHT READING AND EAR TESTS

DAILY EXERCISES FOR PIANO STUDENTS

BY BORIS BERLIN AND ANDREW MARKOW

Series Editor

SCOTT McBRIDE SMITH

National Library of Canada Cataloguing in Publication Data

Berlin, Boris, 1907-2001
 Four star sight reading and ear tests [music]

ISBN 0-88797-789-8 (Introductory level). —
ISBN 0-88797-791-X (bk. 1). — ISBN 0-88797-793-6 (bk. 2)
ISBN 0-88797-795-2 (bk. 3). — ISBN 0-88797-797-9 (bk. 4)
ISBN 0-88797-799-5 (bk. 5). — ISBN 0-88797-801-0 (bk. 6)
ISBN 0-88797-803-7 (bk. 7). — ISBN 0-88797-805-3 (bk. 8)
ISBN 0-88797-807-X (bk. 9). — ISBN 0-88797-809-6 (bk. 10)

1. Piano — Studies and exercises. 2. Ear training.
3. Sight-reading (Music) I. Markow, Andrew, 1942- II. Title.

MT236.B473 2002   786.2'142'076   C2002-900877-8

FREDERICK
HARRIS
MUSIC

ISBN 0-88797-795-2

PREFACE

The ability to read music at sight at the piano is an important skill for all musicians. As piano students work toward fluency in sight reading, develop aural proficiency, and gain a practical knowledge of theory, they will build a foundation of musicianship that will help them to understand music throughout their lives.

Are some pianists naturally better sight readers than others? Not really. But some recognize patterns on the printed page more readily. Such students use their **visual learning skills**. Other students use their natural **tactile sense** to move around the keyboard quickly. Still others have an innate **aural ability** to hear both melody and harmony with only a glance at the score. Some students may also apply **analytical skills** learned from a study of theory to understand form and content.

The goal of the *Four Star* series is to develop each of these skills and abilities in equal measure. In the process of completing the *Four Star* series, students will improve not only their sight-reading skills but also their proficiency in learning and memorizing music. They will also expand their coordination of eyes, ears, and hands, and their powers of concentration and observation. As a result, *Four Star* students will develop confidence in themselves and in their musical abilities and performance.

Each of the 11 *Four Star* volumes contains daily exercises in sight reading and ear training and builds a foundation for an analytical approach to sight reading music, using examples taken from the standard repertoire. (Some excerpts have been modified by the authors for pedagogical reasons.)

Completion of each *Four Star* book effectively prepares students for the corresponding level of examination systems, including:
- RCM Examinations
- Certificate of Merit (Music Teachers Association of California)
- National Guild of Piano Teachers
- most MTNA curriculums

In order to develop students' reading and overall musical abilities more fully, the authors have chosen to exceed the requirements of most examinations systems.

How To Use This Book

The purpose of the *Four Star* series is to provide daily exercises in sight reading and ear training for students to practice at home, as well as tests to be given by the teacher at the lesson. Best results will be obtained through daily student practice, and consistent monitoring and testing at the lesson by the teacher.

SIGHT READING AND RHYTHM

The daily sight-reading and rhythm exercises are intended for students to do by themselves. There are five exercises per week, each including two sight-reading exercises, a short piece to play, and a rhythm to clap. To indicate a rest while clapping, the student should separate their hands and turn their palms upward.

A reference section on Musical Elements and Patterns in This Volume can be found on pp. 4–6. It is useful for teachers to review these at the lesson.

EAR TRAINING

Ear-training exercises can be found following the sight-reading and rhythm drills. These, too, are designed to be practiced by the student alone, as assigned by the teacher.

TESTS

Tests are found beginning on p. 37. These are designed to be given by the teacher at the lesson at the conclusion of the corresponding week's work. Supplementary material may be found in the series *Melody Playback/Singback* and *Rhythm Clapback/Singback* by Boris Berlin and Andrew Markow.

MUSICAL ELEMENTS AND PATTERNS IN THIS VOLUME

MELODIC MOVEMENT

Notes move up.

Notes move down.

Five notes move up, then change direction.

Four notes move down, then change direction.

Several changes of direction
(a zig-zag movement).

Repeated notes (the notes remain the same).

A turn (see p. 23).

CONTRARY MOTION

MELODY AND ACCOMPANIMENT

melody

accompaniment

SEQUENCE (see p. 28)

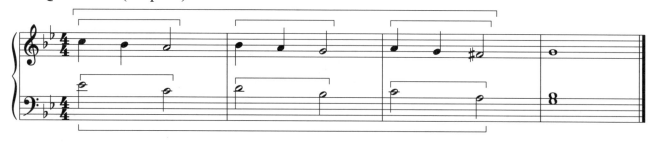

PITCH REPETITION (see p. 27)

PITCH INVERSION (turned upside down) (see p. 10)

INTERVALS

Above a given note: **Below a given note:**

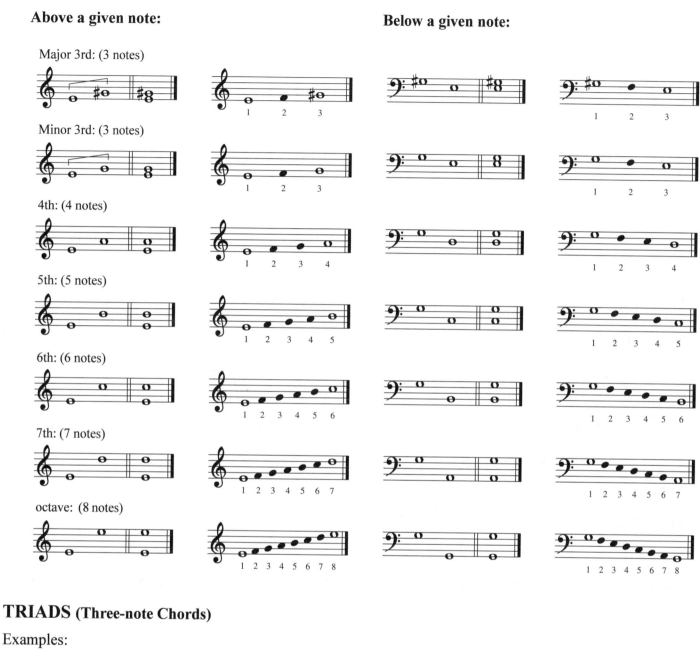

Major 3rd: (3 notes)

Minor 3rd: (3 notes)

4th: (4 notes)

5th: (5 notes)

6th: (6 notes)

7th: (7 notes)

octave: (8 notes)

TRIADS (Three-note Chords)

Examples:

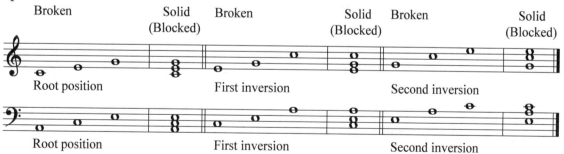

Broken · Solid (Blocked) · Broken · Solid (Blocked) · Broken · Solid (Blocked)

Root position · First inversion · Second inversion

Root position · First inversion · Second inversion

Major Triads
A major 3rd (M3) and a perfect 5th (P5)

Minor Triads
A minor 3rd (m3) and a perfect 5th (P5)

Examples of intervals and broken triads (chords) found in pieces:

G major triad (chord tones)

(see p. 22)

(see p. 13)

TIME VALUES

whole (4 beats)	dotted half (3 beats)	half (2 beats)	quarter (1 beat)	eighth (½ beat)	dotted quarter (1½ beats)

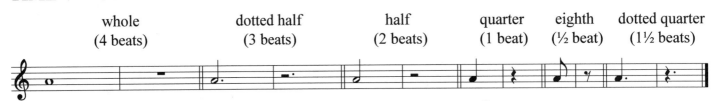

RHYTHMIC PATTERNS

Rhythmic pattern:

Rhythmic pattern:

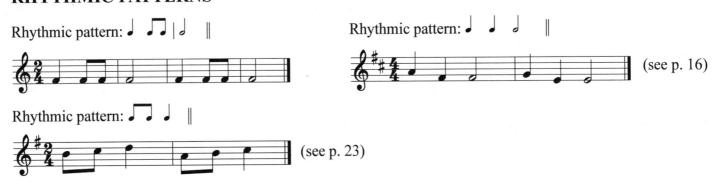

(see p. 16)

Rhythmic pattern:

(see p. 23)

RHYTHMIC IMITATION

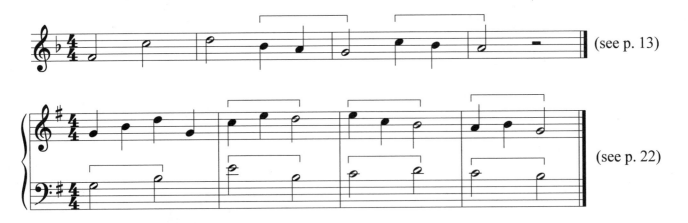

(see p. 13)

(see p. 22)

MARKS OF EXPRESSION AND OTHER MUSICAL SIGNS

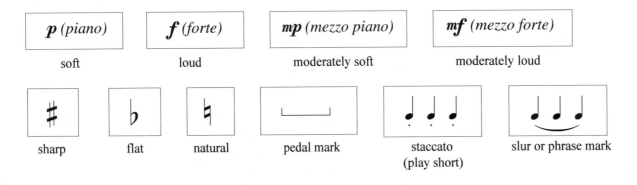

p (piano)	*f* (forte)	*mp* (mezzo piano)	*mf* (mezzo forte)
soft	loud	moderately soft	moderately loud

sharp	flat	natural	pedal mark	staccato (play short)	slur or phrase mark

DAILY SIGHT-READING EXERCISES No. 1

Directions to the student: Complete one set of sight-reading exercises at each practice session.

1   FIRST DAY _____ (date)

Play these notes. What triad do they form?
(Answer: _____)
Which inversion? (Answer: _____)
Now play the triad in solid (blocked) form.

Play these notes. What triad do they form?
(Answer: _____)
Which inversion? (Answer: _____)
Now play the triad in solid (blocked) form.

Name the LH notes as you play.

Clap or tap the rhythmic pattern while counting the beats.

2   SECOND DAY _____ (date)

Play this melodic pattern.

Play this interval of a 4th.

Circle the RH notes which form a C major broken triad.

Clap or tap the rhythmic pattern.

3   THIRD DAY _____ (date)

Play this interval of a 5th.

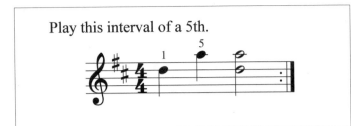

Play this melodic pattern.

Name the LH notes as you play.

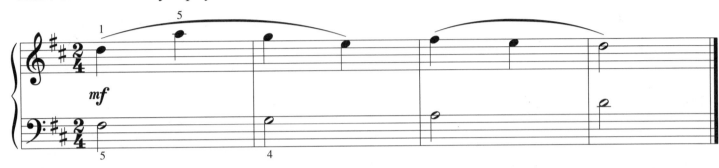

Clap or tap the rhythmic pattern while counting the beats.

---

4   FOURTH DAY _____ (date)

The notes below form the first five notes of a major scale.
Name the scale. (Answer: _____)

Play this melodic pattern with intervals of a 3rd.

Circle the repeated notes.

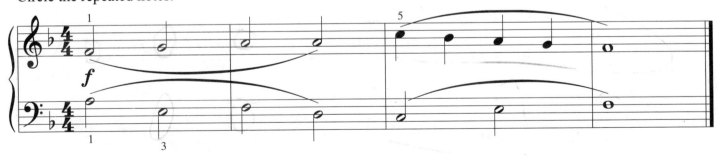

Clap or tap the rhythmic pattern.

5   FIFTH DAY _____ *(date)*

Play these notes. What triad do they form?
(Answer: _____)
Which inversion? (Answer: _____)
Now play the triad in solid (blocked) form.

Play this rhythmic pattern.

Circle the eighth notes.

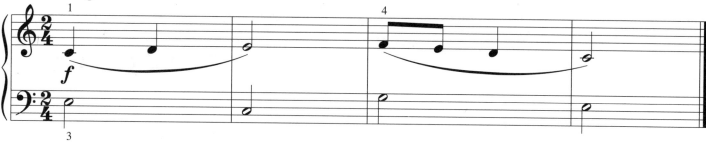

Clap or tap the rhythmic pattern while counting the beats.

DAILY EAR-TRAINING EXERCISES No. 1

Directions to the student: Complete these ear-training exercises at home.

RHYTHM

Sing, clap, or tap the rhythm of these short melodies: (a) by looking at the music and (b) from memory.

INTERVALS

Play the first note of each interval, then sing or hum the second. Identify the interval and write its name underneath.

MELODY PLAYBACK

Name the key of each of the following melodies. For each example, play the tonic chord ONCE. Play the melody TWICE, observing the DIRECTIONS of the notes and the PATTERNS they form. Then play the melody from memory.

DAILY SIGHT-READING EXERCISES No. 2

Directions to the student: Complete one set of sight-reading exercises at each practice session.

 FIRST DAY _____ (*date*)

Play this melodic pattern.

Play this interval of a 5th with the given fingering.

 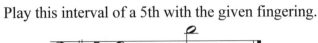

Circle the measure in which the LH moves to a new (higher) hand position.

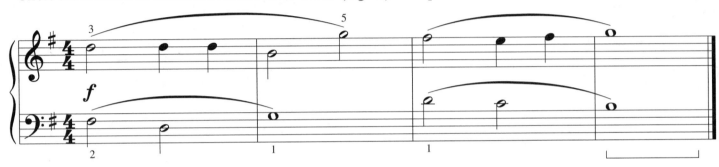

Clap or tap the rhythmic pattern while counting the beats.

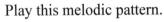 **SECOND DAY** _____ (*date*)

Play this interval of a 5th.

Play this 3-note pattern and its inversion.

How many different intervals are there in the LH? (Answer: _____)
Name them. (Answer: _____)

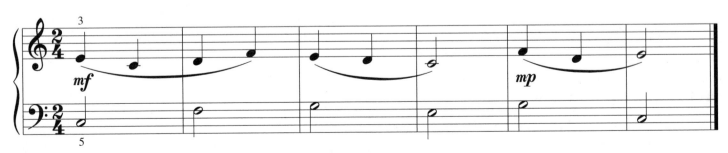

Clap or tap the rhythmic pattern.

3 THIRD DAY _____ (*date*)

Play these notes. What triad do they form?
(Answer: _____)
Which inversion? (Answer: _____)
Now play the triad in solid (blocked) form.

Play this pattern.

Name the RH notes as you play.

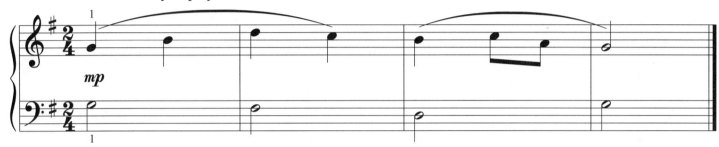

Clap or tap the rhythmic pattern while counting the beats.

---

4 FOURTH DAY _____ (*date*)

Play these notes. What triad do they form?
(Answer: _____)
Which inversion? (Answer: _____)
Now play the triad in solid (blocked) form.

Play these notes. What triad do they form?
(Answer: _____)
Which inversion? (Answer: _____)
Now play the triad in solid (blocked) form.

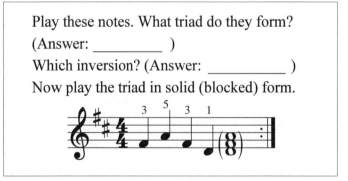

Play, counting the beats.

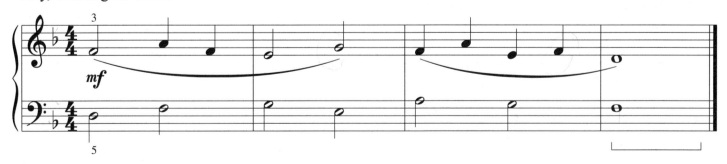

Clap or tap the rhythmic pattern.

5 FIFTH DAY _____ *(date)*

The notes below form the first five notes of a major scale.
Name the scale. (Answer: _____)

Play these intervals of a 4th and 5th.

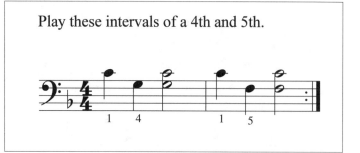

Name the LH notes as you play.

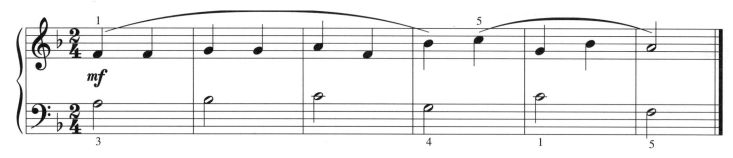

Clap or tap the rhythmic pattern while counting the beats.

DAILY EAR-TRAINING EXERCISES No. 2

Directions to the student: Complete these ear-training exercises at home.

RHYTHM

Sing, clap, or tap the rhythm of these short melodies: (a) by looking at the music and (b) from memory.

INTERVALS

Play the first note of each interval, then sing or hum the second. Repeat the process in reverse. Identify the interval and write its name underneath.

_____   _____   _____   _____

MELODY PLAYBACK

Name the key of each of the following melodies. For each example, play the tonic chord ONCE. Play the melody TWICE, observing the DIRECTIONS of the notes and the PATTERNS they form. Then play the melody from memory.

DAILY SIGHT READING EXERCISES No. 3

Directions to the student: Complete one set of sight-reading exercises at each practice session.

 1   FIRST DAY _____ (*date*)

Play with the given fingering.

The notes below form the first five notes of a major scale.
Name the scale. (Answer: _____)

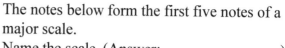

Circle all the intervals of a 4th.

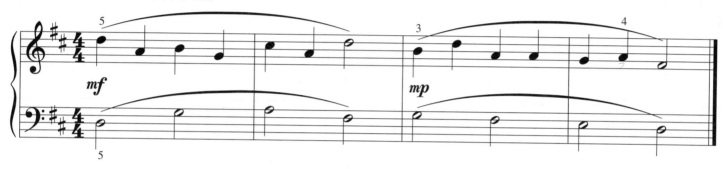

Clap or tap the rhythmic pattern while counting the beats.

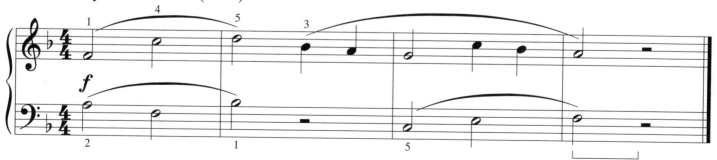

---

2   SECOND DAY _____ (*date*)

Play this interval of a 7th.

Play this melodic pattern.

Circle the rhythmic imitation (♩ ♩ ♩).

Clap or tap the rhythmic pattern.

3 THIRD DAY _____ (date)

Play with the given fingering.

Play this sequence of descending 3rds.

Circle all the intervals of a 3rd.

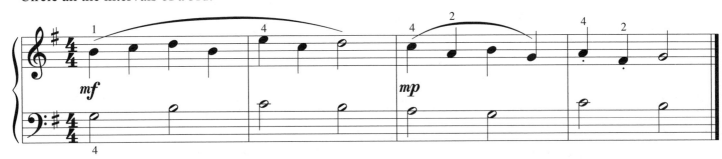

Clap or tap the rhythmic pattern while counting the beats.

4 FOURTH DAY _____ (date)

Play this C major broken triad followed by an interval of a 6th.

Play these descending 3rds followed by an interval of a 7th.

Name the RH notes as you play.

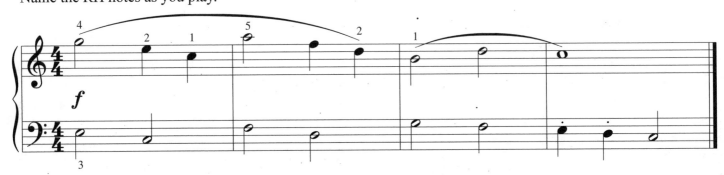

Clap or tap the rhythmic pattern.

5 FIFTH DAY _____ (date)

Play this rhythmic pattern.

Play these notes. What triad do they form?
(Answer: _____)
Which inversion? (Answer: _____)
Now play the triad in solid (blocked) form.

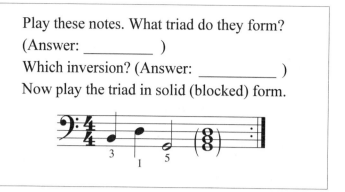

Play, counting the beats.

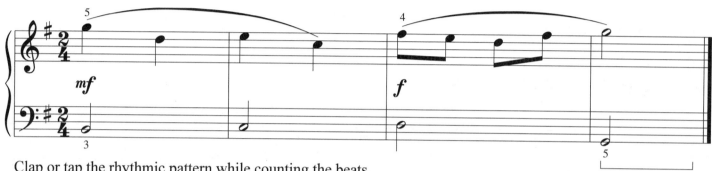

Clap or tap the rhythmic pattern while counting the beats.

DAILY EAR-TRAINING EXERCISES No. 3

Directions to the student: Complete these ear-training exercises at home.

RHYTHM

Sing, clap, or tap the rhythm of these short melodies: (a) by looking at the music and (b) from memory.

INTERVALS

Play the first note of each interval, then sing or hum the second. Identify the interval and write its name underneath.

MELODY PLAYBACK

Name the key of each of the following melodies. For each example, play the tonic chord ONCE. Play the melody TWICE, observing the DIRECTIONS of the notes and the PATTERNS they form. Then play the melody from memory.

DAILY SIGHT-READING EXERCISES No. 4

Directions to the student: Complete one set of sight-reading exercises at each practice session.

 1   FIRST DAY _____ (*date*)

 Play these intervals of a 5th and a 4th.

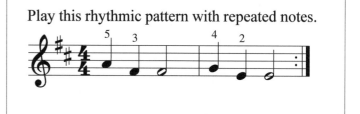 Play this rhythmic pattern with repeated notes.

Circle the melodic imitation.

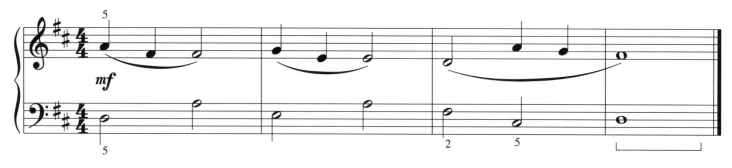

Clap or tap the rhythmic pattern while counting the beats.

2   SECOND DAY _____ (*date*)

 Play these intervals of a 5th and a 6th.

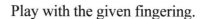  Play with the given fingering.

Play, counting the beats.

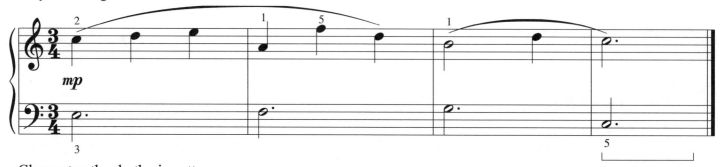

Clap or tap the rhythmic pattern.

3 THIRD DAY _____ (date)

The notes below form the first five notes of a major scale.
Name the scale. (Answer: _____)

Play with the given fingering.

Circle the notes that form the first five notes of the ascending D major scale in the RH.

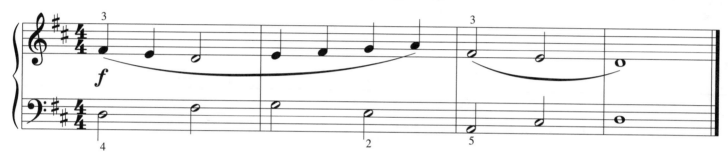

Clap or tap the rhythmic pattern while counting the beats.

4 FOURTH DAY _____ (date)

Play with the given fingering.

Play this melodic pattern which forms a turn.

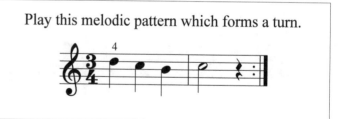

Circle the notes in the RH which form the A minor broken triad.

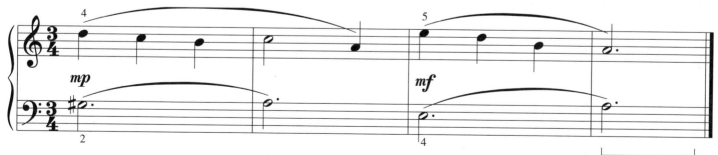

Clap or tap the rhythmic pattern.

5 | FIFTH DAY _____ (date)

Play with the given fingering.

Play these notes. What triad do they form?
(Answer: _____)
Which inversion? (Answer: _____)
Now play the triad in solid (blocked) form.

Circle the broken C major triad in the RH, then play, counting the beats.

Clap or tap the rhythmic pattern while counting the beats.

DAILY EAR-TRAINING EXERCISES No. 4

Directions to the student: Complete these ear-training exercises at home.

RHYTHM

Sing, clap, or tap the rhythm of these short melodies: (a) by looking at the music and (b) from memory.

INTERVALS

Play the first note of each interval, then sing or hum the second. Repeat the process in reverse. Identify the interval and write its name underneath.

_____ _____   _____ _____

MELODY PLAYBACK

Name the key of each of the following melodies. For each example, play the tonic chord ONCE. Play the melody TWICE, observing the DIRECTIONS of the notes and the PATTERNS they form. Then play the melody from memory.

DAILY SIGHT-READING EXERCISES No. 5

Directions to the student: Complete one set of sight-reading exercises at each practice session.

1 FIRST DAY _____ (date)

Play with the given fingering.

Play with the given fingering.

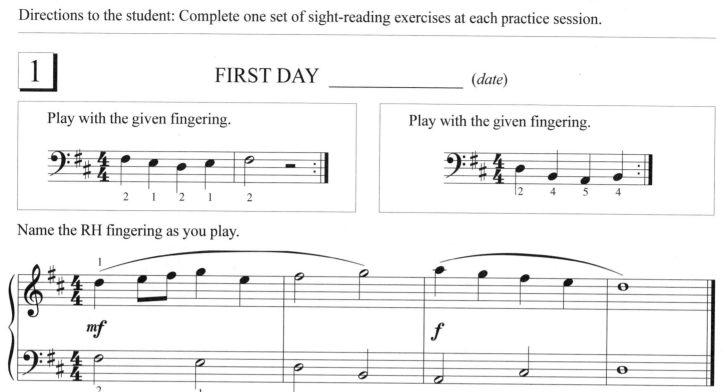

Name the RH fingering as you play.

Clap or tap the rhythmic pattern while counting the beats.

2 SECOND DAY _____ (date)

Play these notes. What triad do they form?
(Answer: _____) Which inversion?
(Answer: _____)
Now play the triad in solid (blocked) form.

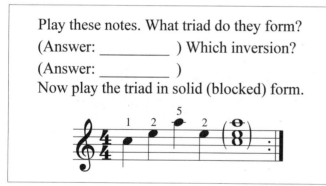

Play this interval of a 6th.

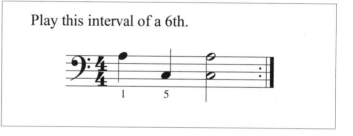

In what key is this piece written? (Answer: _____)

Clap or tap the rhythmic pattern.

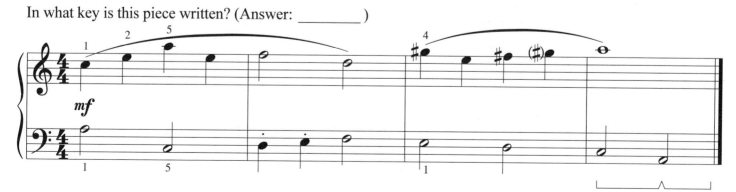

3   THIRD DAY _____ (*date*)

Play these notes. What triad do they form?
(Answer: _____)
Which inversion? (Answer: _____)
Now play the triad in solid (blocked) form.

Play these notes. What triad do they form?
(Answer: _____)
Which inversion? (Answer: _____)
Now play the triad in solid (blocked) form.

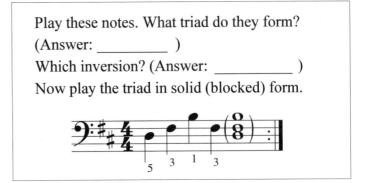

Name the LH notes as you play.

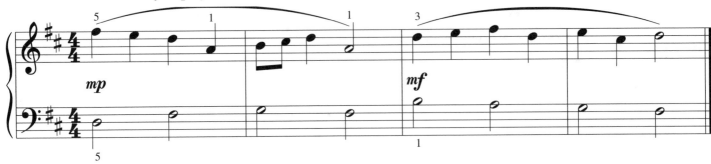

Clap or tap the rhythmic pattern while counting the beats.

---

4   FOURTH DAY _____ (*date*)

Play with the given fingering.

Play with the given fingering.

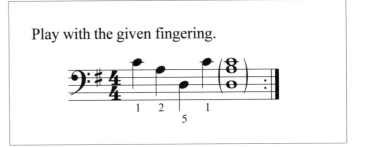

Circle the intervals of a 3rd, 5th, and 4th in the last two measures of the LH.

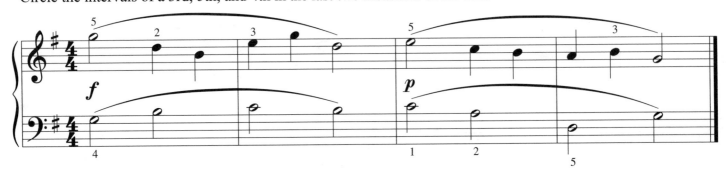

Clap or tap the rhythmic pattern.

5

FIFTH DAY _____ (date)

Play with the given fingering.

The notes below form the first five notes of a major scale.
Name the scale. (Answer: _____)

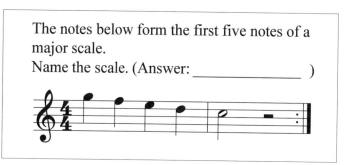

Circle the two measures in which the fingering is repeated in the LH.

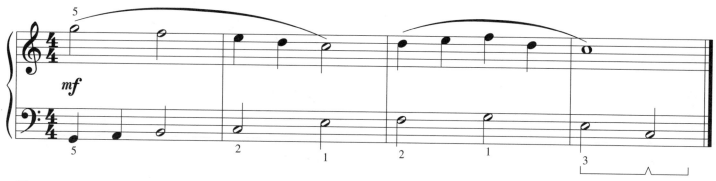

Clap or tap the rhythmic pattern while counting the beats.

DAILY EAR-TRAINING EXERCISES NO. 5

Directions to the student: Complete these ear-training exercises at home.

RHYTHM

Sing, clap, or tap the rhythm of these short melodies: (a) by looking at the music and (b) from memory.

INTERVALS

Play the first note of each interval, then sing or hum the second. Identify the interval and write its name underneath.

MELODY PLAYBACK

Name the key of each of the following melodies. For each example, play the tonic chord ONCE. Play the melody TWICE, observing the DIRECTIONS of the notes and the PATTERNS they form. Then play the melody from memory.

DAILY SIGHT-READING EXERCISES No. 6

Directions to the student: Complete one set of sight-reading exercises at each practice session.

1 FIRST DAY _____ (date)

Play this melodic pattern which includes a quarter rest.

Play these notes. What triad do they form?
(Answer: _____)
Which inversion? (Answer: _____)
Now play the triad in solid (blocked) form.

Mark the directions of the RH and LH melodies with arrows.

Clap or tap the rhythmic pattern while counting the beats.

2 SECOND DAY _____ (date)

Play these notes. What triad do they form?
(Answer: _____)
Which inversion? (Answer: _____)
Now play the triad in solid (blocked) form.

Play these notes. What triad do they form?
(Answer: _____)
Which inversion? (Answer: _____)
Now play the triad in solid (blocked) form.

Circle the notes that form the G major triad and those that form the C major triad.

Clap or tap the rhythmic pattern.

3

Play this melodic pattern which forms a turn.

Play this melodic pattern.

Play, counting the beats.

Clap or tap the rhythmic pattern while counting the beats.

4

FOURTH DAY _____ (*date*)

Play this interval of a 7th.

Play with the given fingering.

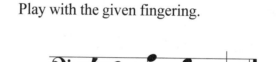

Circle the intervals of a 5th, 6th, and 7th.

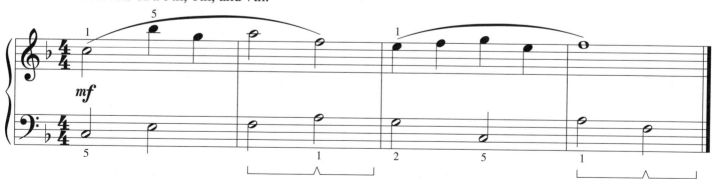

Clap or tap the rhythmic pattern.

5   FIFTH DAY _____ (date)

Play with the given fingering.

Play with the given fingering.

Name the LH notes as you play.

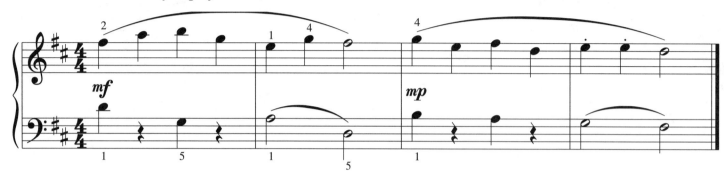

Clap or tap the rhythmic pattern while counting the beats.

DAILY EAR-TRAINING EXERCISES No. 6

Directions to the student: Complete these ear-training exercises at home.

RHYTHM

Sing, clap, or tap the rhythm of these short melodies: (a) by looking at the music and (b) from memory.

INTERVALS

Play the first note of each interval, then sing or hum the second. Identify the interval and write its name underneath.

MELODY PLAYBACK

Name the key of each of the following melodies. For each example, play the tonic chord ONCE. Play the melody TWICE, observing the DIRECTIONS of the notes and the PATTERNS they form. Then play the melody from memory.

DAILY SIGHT-READING EXERCISES No. 7

Directions to the student: Complete one set of sight-reading exercises at each practice session.

1   FIRST DAY _____ (date)

Play with the given fingering.

Play with the given fingering.

Circle the RH notes in m. 2 which form the D major triad.

Clap or tap the rhythmic pattern while counting the beats.

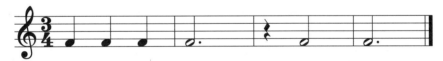

2   SECOND DAY _____ (date)

Play with the given fingering.

Play with the given fingering.

Circle the solid (blocked) interval of a 3rd.

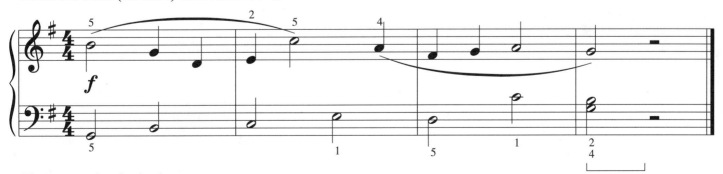

Clap or tap the rhythmic pattern.

3 THIRD DAY _____ (date)

Play with the given fingering.

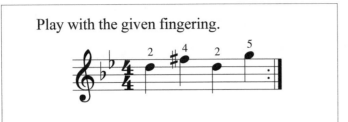

Play with the given fingering.

Circle the accidentals.

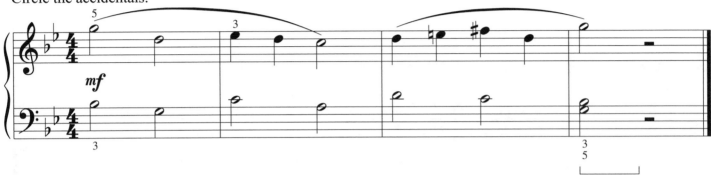

Clap or tap the rhythmic pattern while counting the beats.

---

4 FOURTH DAY _____ (date)

Play this interval of a 6th.

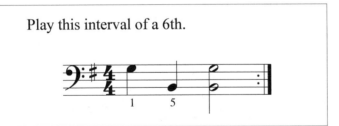

Play with the given fingering.

Bracket (⌐‾‾‾⌐) the groups of notes in the RH which move in contrary motion with the LH.

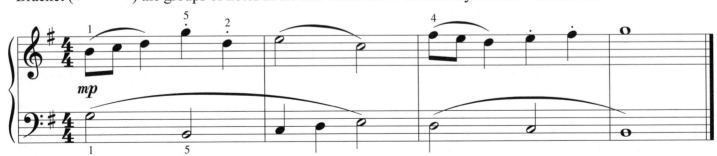

Clap or tap the rhythmic pattern.

5

FIFTH DAY _____ (date)

Play with the given fingering.

Play with the given fingering.

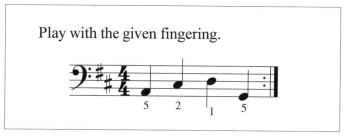

Bracket the five-note melodic imitations in the RH.

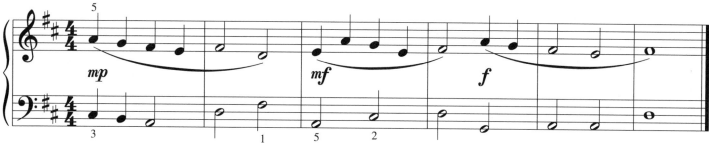

Clap or tap the rhythmic pattern while counting the beats.

DAILY EAR-TRAINING EXERCISES NO. 7

Directions to the student: Complete these ear-training exercises at home.

RHYTHM

Sing, clap, or tap the rhythm of these short melodies: (a) by looking at the music and (b) from memory.

INTERVALS

Play the first note of each interval, then sing or hum the second. Repeat the process in reverse. Identify the interval and write its name underneath.

_____ _____

_____ _____

MELODY PLAYBACK

Name the key of each of the following melodies. For each example, play the tonic chord ONCE. Play the melody TWICE, observing the DIRECTIONS of the notes and the PATTERNS they form. Then play the melody from memory.

DAILY SIGHT-READING EXERCISES No. 8

Directions to the student: Complete one set of sight-reading exercises at each practice session.

1   **FIRST DAY** _____ (_date_)

Play these notes. What triad do they form?
(Answer: _____)
Which inversion? (Answer: _____)
Now play the triad in solid (blocked) form.

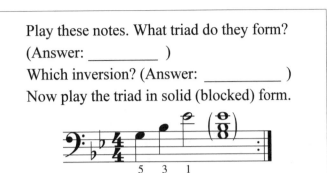

Play with the given fingering.

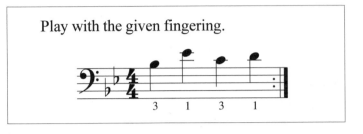

How many measures does the sequence in this piece last? (Answer: _____) Place an "X" in these measures.

Clap or tap the rhythmic pattern while counting the beats.

---

2   **SECOND DAY** _____ (_date_)

Play with the given fingering and articulation.

Play with the given fingering and articulation.

Circle all the staccato notes.

Clap or tap the rhythmic pattern.

3 THIRD DAY _____ (date)

Play these intervals of a 6th and 4th.

Play this cadence.

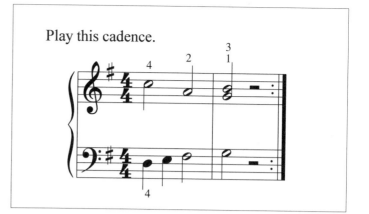

How many broken triads are there in the RH? (Answer: ___) Name them. (Answer: _____)

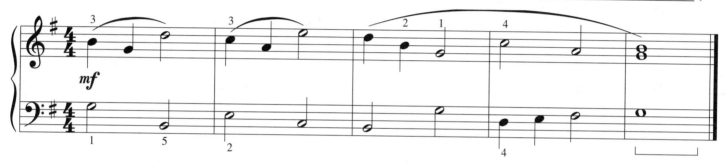

Clap or tap the rhythmic pattern while counting the beats.

4 FOURTH DAY _____ (date)

Play with the given fingering.

Play with the given fingering.

Circle the ascending broken melodic 3rds in the RH. How many are there? (Answer: _____)

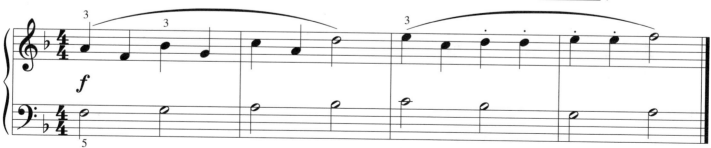

Clap or tap the rhythmic pattern.

5 FIFTH DAY _____ (date)

Play these notes. What triad do they form?

(Answer: _____)

Which inversion? (Answer: _____)

Now play the triad in solid (blocked) form.

Play this pattern.

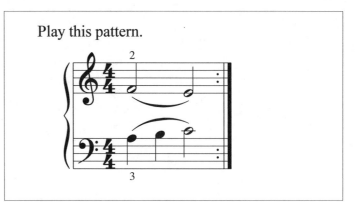

Circle the notes in the RH that form a C major triad in first inversion.

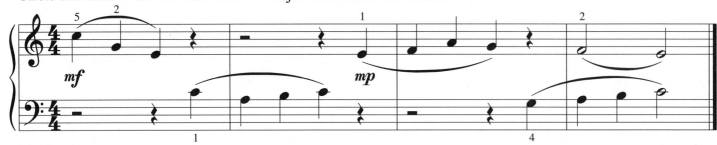

Clap or tap the rhythmic pattern while counting the beats.

DAILY EAR-TRAINING EXERCISES No. 8

Directions to the student: Complete these ear-training exercises at home.

RHYTHM

Sing, clap, or tap the rhythm of these short melodies: (a) by looking at the music and (b) from memory.

INTERVALS

Play the first note of each interval, then sing or hum the second. Repeat the process in reverse. Identify the interval and write its name underneath.

MELODY PLAYBACK

Name the key of each of the following melodies. For each example, play the tonic chord ONCE. Play the melody TWICE, observing the DIRECTIONS of the notes and the PATTERNS they form. Then play the melody from memory.

DAILY SIGHT-READING EXERCISES No. 9

Directions to the student: Complete one set of sight-reading exercises at each practice session.

1   FIRST DAY _____ (date)

Play with the given fingering.

Play with the given fingering.

Circle the RH notes which form the G minor triad in second inversion, and the E flat major triad in second inversion.

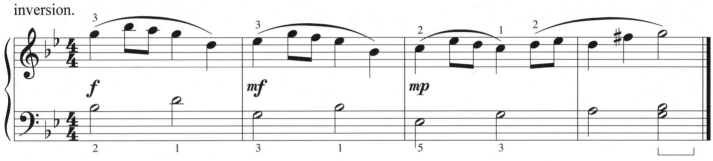

Clap or tap the rhythmic pattern while counting the beats.

2   SECOND DAY _____ (date)

Play with the given fingering.

Play this cadence.

Circle the quarter rests, then play, counting the beats.

Clap or tap the rhythmic pattern.

3 THIRD DAY _____ (*date*)

Play with the given fingering and articulation.

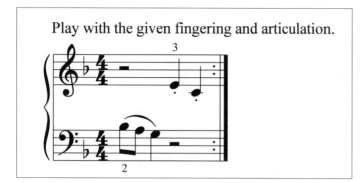

Play this cadence.

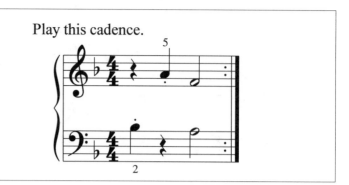

Circle the intervals of a 5th, 4th, and 3rd.

Clap or tap the rhythmic pattern while counting the beats.

---

4 FOURTH DAY _____ (*date*)

Play with the given fingering.

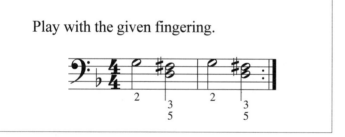

Play this cadence.

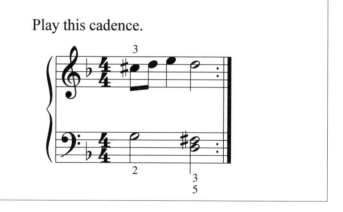

Circle the repeated notes.

Clap or tap the rhythmic pattern.

5 | FIFTH DAY _____ (date)

Play with the given fingering.

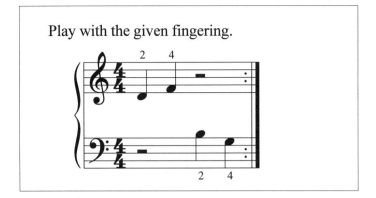

Play this cadence.

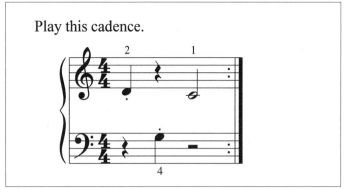

Circle the rests, and then play, counting the beats.

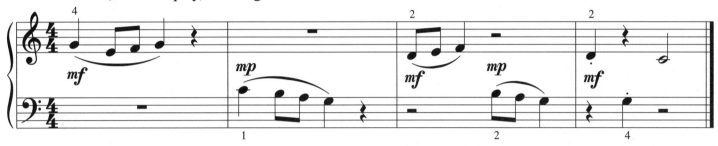

Clap or tap the rhythmic pattern while counting the beats.

DAILY EAR-TRAINING EXERCISES No. 9

Directions to the student: Complete these ear-training exercises at home.

RHYTHM

Sing, clap, or tap the rhythm of these short melodies: (a) by looking at the music and (b) from memory.

INTERVALS

Play the first note of each interval, then sing or hum the second. Repeat the process in reverse. Identify the interval and write its name underneath.

MELODY PLAYBACK

Name the key of each of the following melodies. For each example, play the tonic chord ONCE. Play the melody TWICE, observing the DIRECTIONS of the notes and the PATTERNS they form. Then play the melody from memory.

DAILY SIGHT-READING EXERCISES No. 10

Directions to the student: Complete one set of sight-reading exercises at each practice session.

1   FIRST DAY _____ (*date*)

Play with the given fingering.

Play this cadence.

Circle the rhythmic imitations (♩♪♪♪♪ ♩ ♩) and (♪♪ ♩ ♩).

Clap or tap the rhythmic pattern while counting the beats.

2   SECOND DAY _____ (*date*)

Play with the given fingering.

Play this cadence.

Circle the RH notes in m. 1 which form the first six notes of the G major scale.

Clap or tap the rhythmic pattern.

3 THIRD DAY _____ (date)

Play this melodic pattern.

Play these notes. What triad do they form?
(Answer: _____)
Which inversion? (Answer: _____)
Now play the triad in solid (blocked) form.

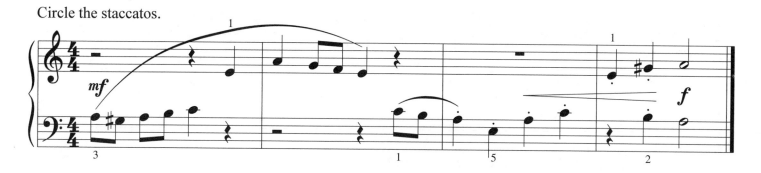

Circle the staccatos.

Clap or tap the rhythmic pattern while counting the beats.

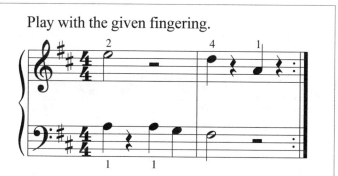

---

4 FOURTH DAY _____ (date)

Play with the given fingering.

Play with the given fingering.

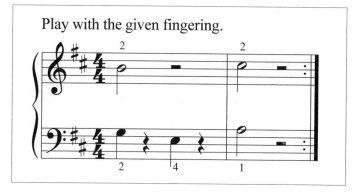

Play, counting the beats.

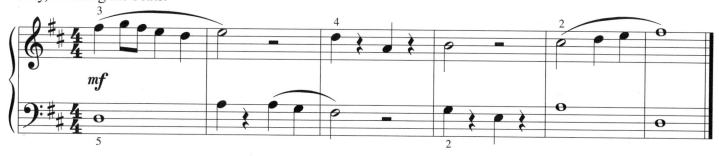

Clap or tap the rhythmic pattern.

5 FIFTH DAY _____ (date)

Play with the given fingering.

Play this cadence.

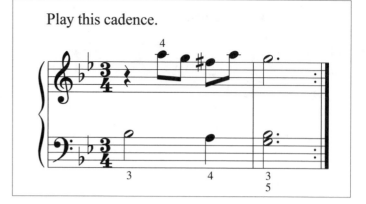

Play, counting the beats.

Clap or tap the rhythmic pattern while counting the beats.

DAILY EAR-TRAINING EXERCISES No. 10

Directions to the student: Complete these ear-training exercises at home.

RHYTHM

Sing, clap, or tap the rhythm of these short melodies: (a) by looking at the music and (b) from memory.

INTERVALS

Play the first note of each interval, then sing or hum the second. Repeat the process in reverse. Identify the interval and write its name underneath.

MELODY PLAYBACK

Name the key of each of the following melodies. For each example, play the tonic chord ONCE. Play the melody TWICE, observing the DIRECTIONS of the notes and the PATTERNS they form. Then play the melody from memory.

★ Four Star Test No. 1 ★

GIVEN BY THE TEACHER AT THE LESSON

SIGHT-READING TEST

Teacher's grading

Play with the given fingering.

Clap or tap the rhythmic pattern.

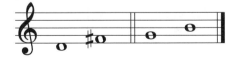

EAR TEST

During these tests, the student must not see the keyboard or look at the music.

RHYTHM

The teacher selects one of the following short melodies and plays it TWICE.
The student then sings, claps, or taps the rhythm of the short melody from memory.

INTERVALS

The teacher selects and names each of the following intervals and plays the first note ONCE.
The student then sings or hums the other note; OR
The teacher plays an interval in broken form ONCE and the student *identifies* (names) it by ear.
The teacher then repeats this procedure with several other intervals.

MELODY PLAYBACK

The teacher selects one of the following melodies, names the key, plays the tonic chord ONCE, and then plays the melody TWICE. The student then plays back the melody from memory.

For additional material, see the series *Melody Playback/Singback* and *Rhythm Clapback/Singback*.

★ FOUR STAR TEST NO. 2 ★

GIVEN BY THE TEACHER AT THE LESSON

SIGHT-READING TEST

Teacher's grading

Play with the given fingering.

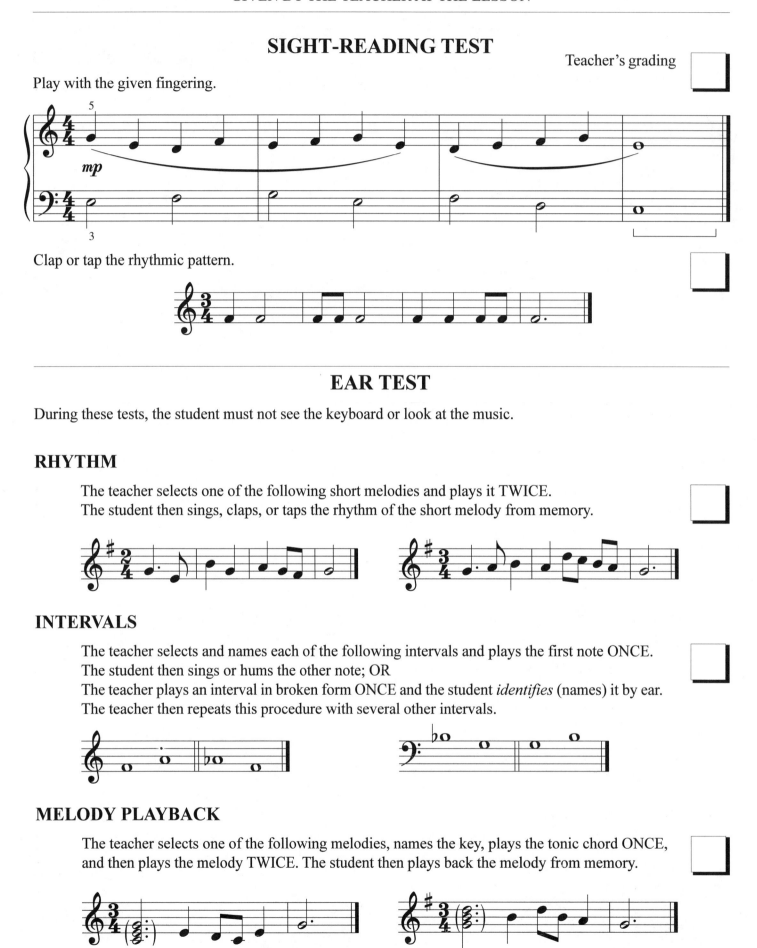

Clap or tap the rhythmic pattern.

EAR TEST

During these tests, the student must not see the keyboard or look at the music.

RHYTHM

The teacher selects one of the following short melodies and plays it TWICE.
The student then sings, claps, or taps the rhythm of the short melody from memory.

INTERVALS

The teacher selects and names each of the following intervals and plays the first note ONCE.
The student then sings or hums the other note; OR
The teacher plays an interval in broken form ONCE and the student *identifies* (names) it by ear.
The teacher then repeats this procedure with several other intervals.

MELODY PLAYBACK

The teacher selects one of the following melodies, names the key, plays the tonic chord ONCE,
and then plays the melody TWICE. The student then plays back the melody from memory.

For additional material, see the series *Melody Playback/Singback* and *Rhythm Clapback/Singback*.

★ Four Star Test No. 3 ★

GIVEN BY THE TEACHER AT THE LESSON

SIGHT-READING TEST

Teacher's grading

Play with the given fingering.

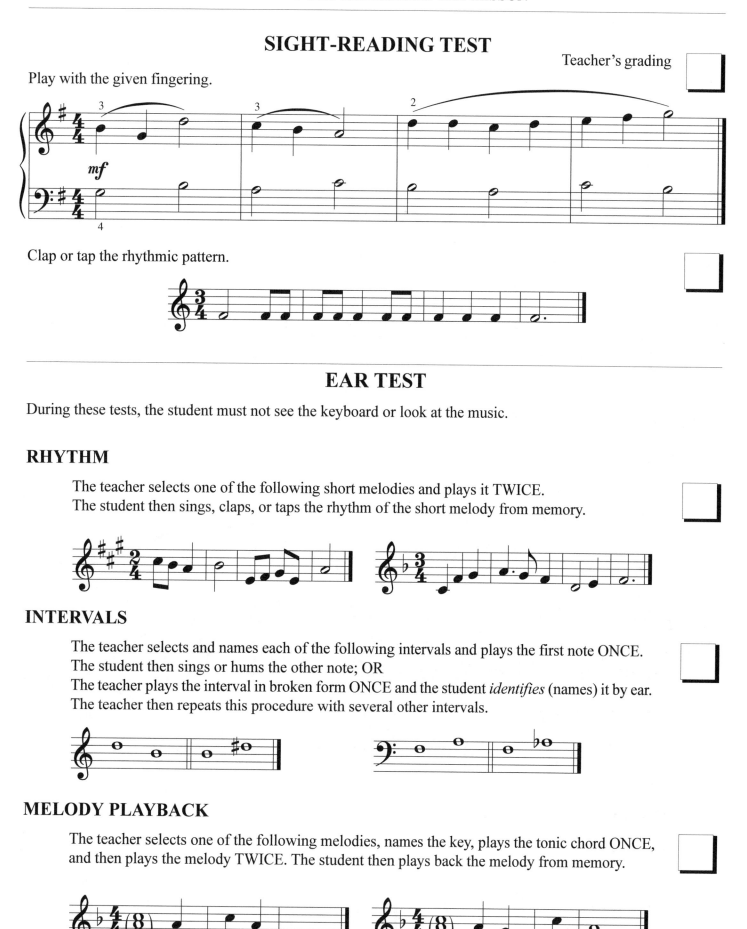

Clap or tap the rhythmic pattern.

EAR TEST

During these tests, the student must not see the keyboard or look at the music.

RHYTHM

The teacher selects one of the following short melodies and plays it TWICE.
The student then sings, claps, or taps the rhythm of the short melody from memory.

INTERVALS

The teacher selects and names each of the following intervals and plays the first note ONCE.
The student then sings or hums the other note; OR
The teacher plays the interval in broken form ONCE and the student *identifies* (names) it by ear.
The teacher then repeats this procedure with several other intervals.

MELODY PLAYBACK

The teacher selects one of the following melodies, names the key, plays the tonic chord ONCE,
and then plays the melody TWICE. The student then plays back the melody from memory.

For additional material, see the series *Melody Playback/Singback* and *Rhythm Clapback/Singback*.

★ FOUR STAR TEST NO. 4 ★

GIVEN BY THE TEACHER AT THE LESSON

SIGHT-READING TEST

Teacher's grading

Play with the given fingering.

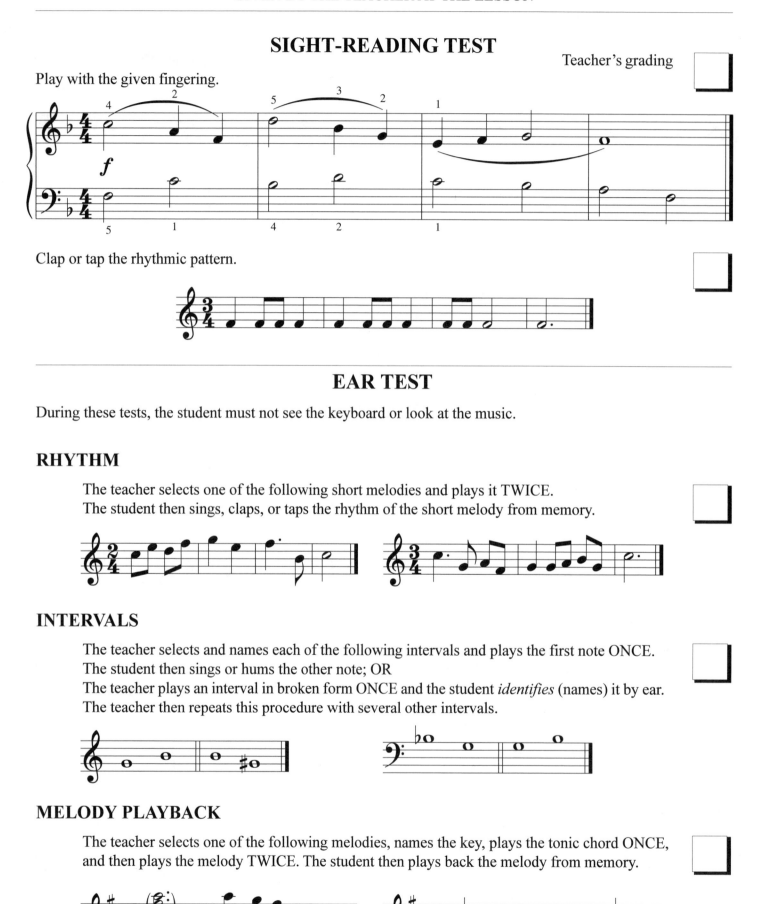

Clap or tap the rhythmic pattern.

EAR TEST

During these tests, the student must not see the keyboard or look at the music.

RHYTHM

The teacher selects one of the following short melodies and plays it TWICE.
The student then sings, claps, or taps the rhythm of the short melody from memory.

INTERVALS

The teacher selects and names each of the following intervals and plays the first note ONCE.
The student then sings or hums the other note; OR
The teacher plays an interval in broken form ONCE and the student *identifies* (names) it by ear.
The teacher then repeats this procedure with several other intervals.

MELODY PLAYBACK

The teacher selects one of the following melodies, names the key, plays the tonic chord ONCE,
and then plays the melody TWICE. The student then plays back the melody from memory.

For additional material, see the series *Melody Playback/Singback* and *Rhythm Clapback/Singback*.

★ FOUR STAR TEST NO. 5 ★

GIVEN BY THE TEACHER AT THE LESSON

SIGHT-READING TEST

Teacher's grading

Play with the given fingering.

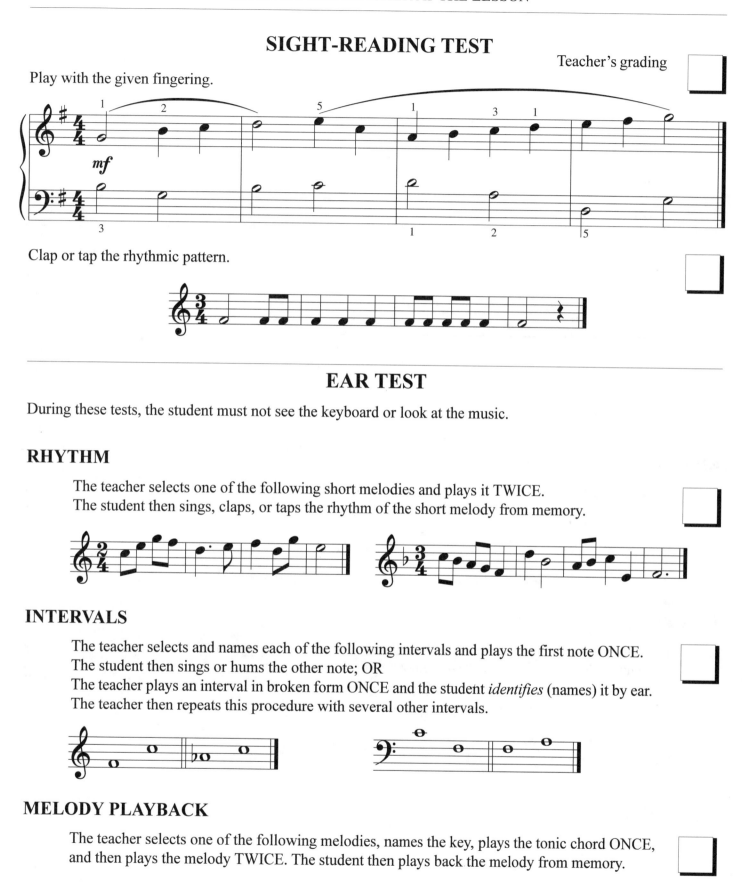

Clap or tap the rhythmic pattern.

EAR TEST

During these tests, the student must not see the keyboard or look at the music.

RHYTHM

The teacher selects one of the following short melodies and plays it TWICE.
The student then sings, claps, or taps the rhythm of the short melody from memory.

INTERVALS

The teacher selects and names each of the following intervals and plays the first note ONCE.
The student then sings or hums the other note; OR
The teacher plays an interval in broken form ONCE and the student *identifies* (names) it by ear.
The teacher then repeats this procedure with several other intervals.

MELODY PLAYBACK

The teacher selects one of the following melodies, names the key, plays the tonic chord ONCE, and then plays the melody TWICE. The student then plays back the melody from memory.

For additional material, see the series *Melody Playback/Singback* and *Rhythm Clapback/Singback*.

★ Four Star Test No. 6 ★

GIVEN BY THE TEACHER AT THE LESSON

SIGHT-READING TEST

Teacher's grading

Play with the given fingering.

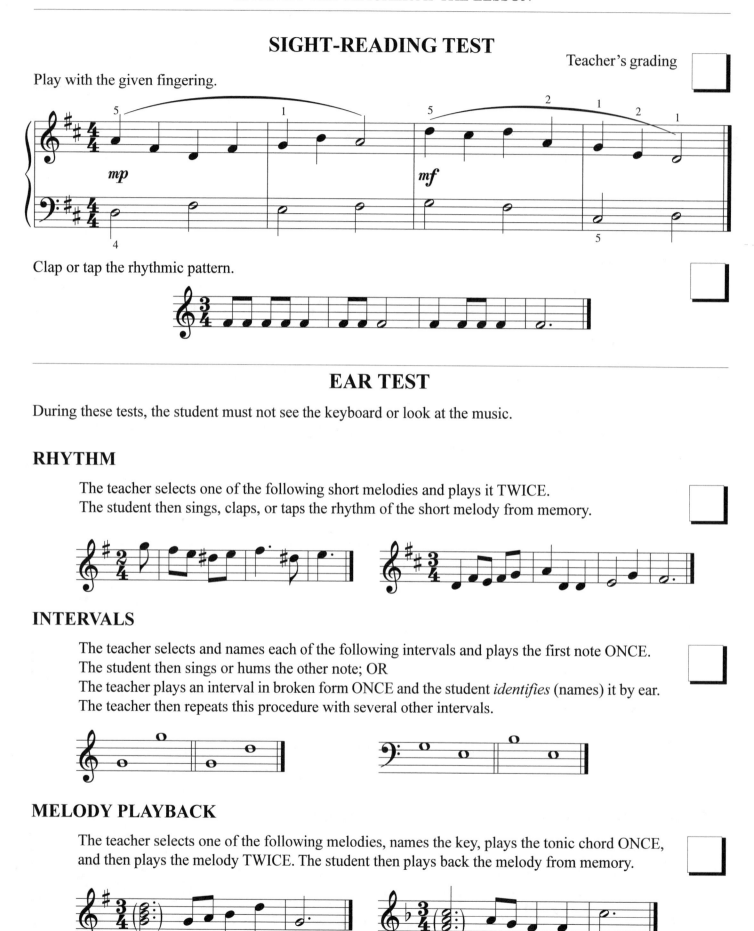

Clap or tap the rhythmic pattern.

EAR TEST

During these tests, the student must not see the keyboard or look at the music.

RHYTHM

The teacher selects one of the following short melodies and plays it TWICE.
The student then sings, claps, or taps the rhythm of the short melody from memory.

INTERVALS

The teacher selects and names each of the following intervals and plays the first note ONCE.
The student then sings or hums the other note; OR
The teacher plays an interval in broken form ONCE and the student *identifies* (names) it by ear.
The teacher then repeats this procedure with several other intervals.

MELODY PLAYBACK

The teacher selects one of the following melodies, names the key, plays the tonic chord ONCE, and then plays the melody TWICE. The student then plays back the melody from memory.

For additional material, see the series *Melody Playback/Singback* and *Rhythm Clapback/Singback.*

★ FOUR STAR TEST NO. 7 ★

GIVEN BY THE TEACHER AT THE LESSON

SIGHT-READING TEST

Teacher's grading

Play with the given fingering.

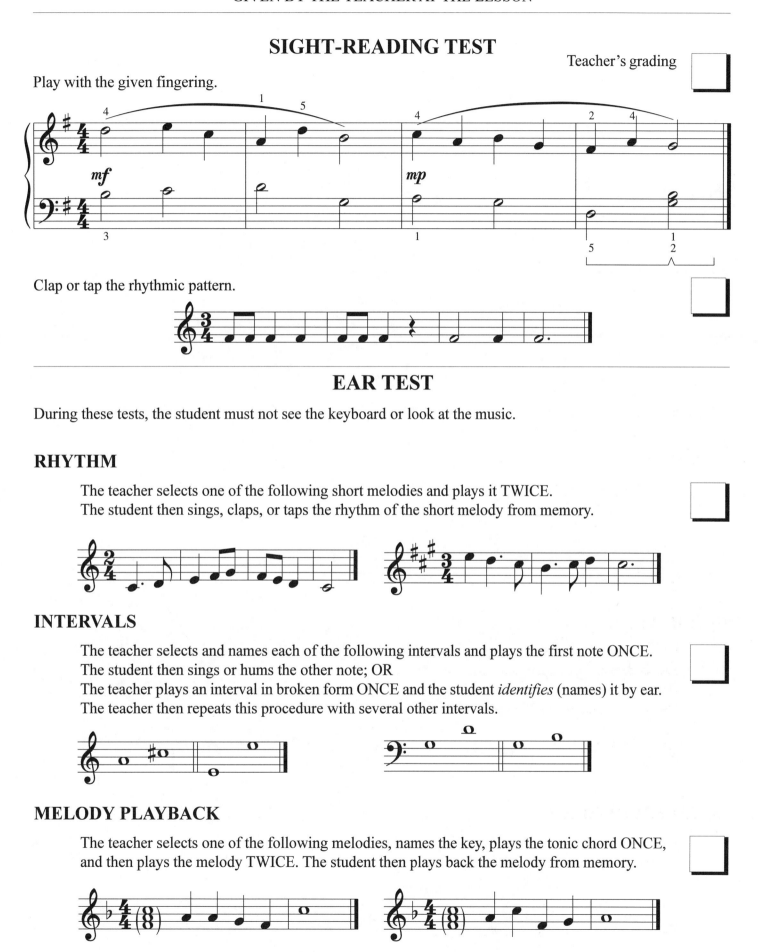

Clap or tap the rhythmic pattern.

EAR TEST

During these tests, the student must not see the keyboard or look at the music.

RHYTHM

The teacher selects one of the following short melodies and plays it TWICE.
The student then sings, claps, or taps the rhythm of the short melody from memory.

INTERVALS

The teacher selects and names each of the following intervals and plays the first note ONCE.
The student then sings or hums the other note; OR
The teacher plays an interval in broken form ONCE and the student *identifies* (names) it by ear.
The teacher then repeats this procedure with several other intervals.

MELODY PLAYBACK

The teacher selects one of the following melodies, names the key, plays the tonic chord ONCE, and then plays the melody TWICE. The student then plays back the melody from memory.

For additional material, see the series *Melody Playback/Singback* and *Rhythm Clapback/Singback*.

★ FOUR STAR TEST NO. 8 ★

GIVEN BY THE TEACHER AT THE LESSON

SIGHT-READING TEST

Teacher's grading

Play with the given fingering.

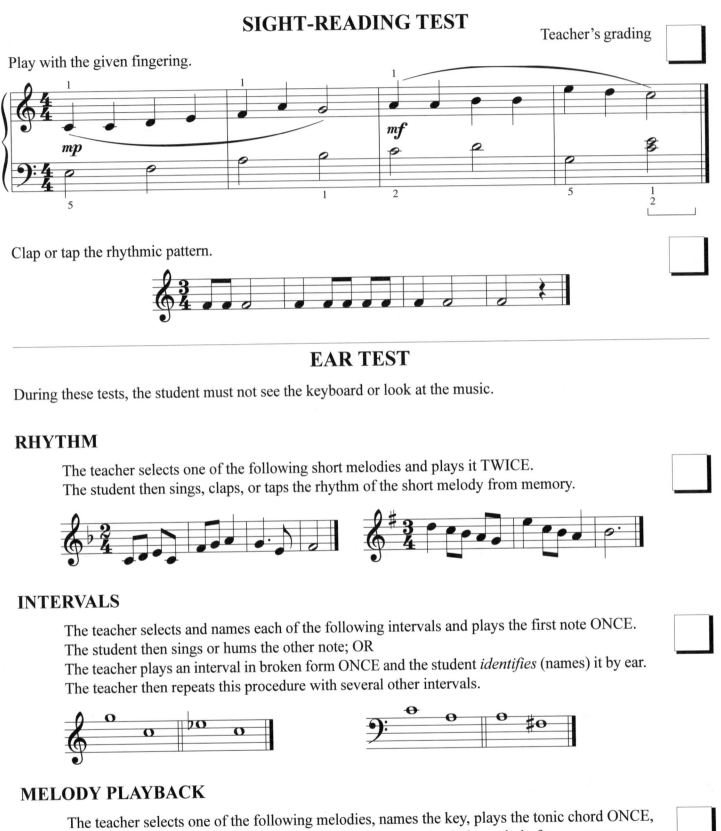

Clap or tap the rhythmic pattern.

EAR TEST

During these tests, the student must not see the keyboard or look at the music.

RHYTHM

The teacher selects one of the following short melodies and plays it TWICE.
The student then sings, claps, or taps the rhythm of the short melody from memory.

INTERVALS

The teacher selects and names each of the following intervals and plays the first note ONCE.
The student then sings or hums the other note; OR
The teacher plays an interval in broken form ONCE and the student *identifies* (names) it by ear.
The teacher then repeats this procedure with several other intervals.

MELODY PLAYBACK

The teacher selects one of the following melodies, names the key, plays the tonic chord ONCE,
and then plays the melody TWICE. The student then plays back the melody from memory.

For additional material, see the series *Melody Playback/Singback* and *Rhythm Clapback/Singback*.

★ FOUR STAR TEST NO. 9 ★

GIVEN BY THE TEACHER AT THE LESSON

SIGHT-READING TEST

Teacher's grading

Play with the given fingering.

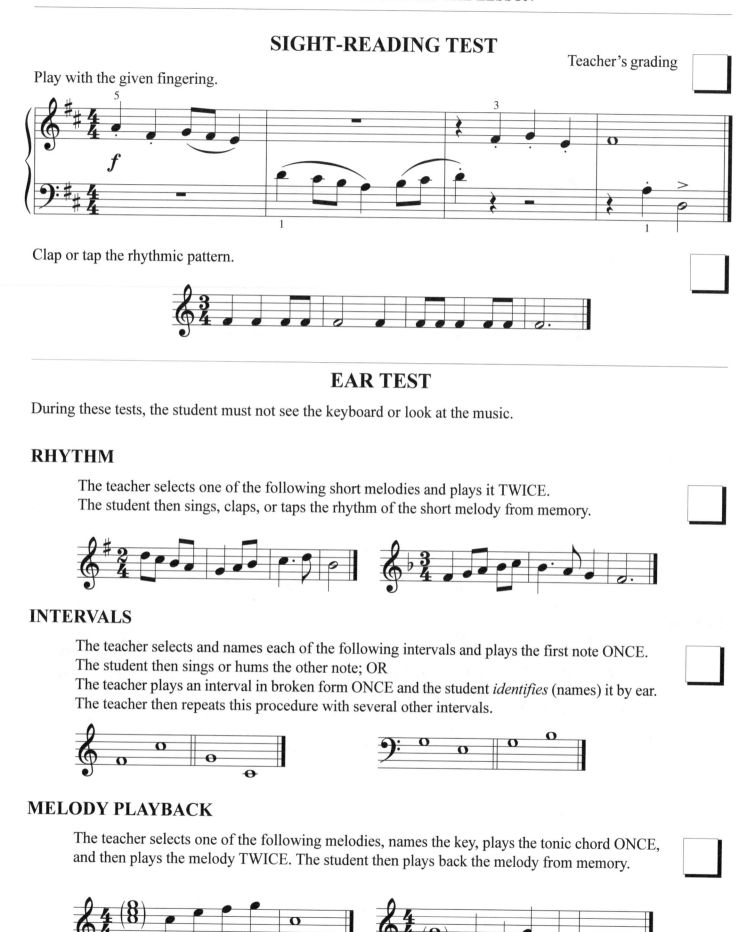

Clap or tap the rhythmic pattern.

EAR TEST

During these tests, the student must not see the keyboard or look at the music.

RHYTHM

The teacher selects one of the following short melodies and plays it TWICE.
The student then sings, claps, or taps the rhythm of the short melody from memory.

INTERVALS

The teacher selects and names each of the following intervals and plays the first note ONCE.
The student then sings or hums the other note; OR
The teacher plays an interval in broken form ONCE and the student *identifies* (names) it by ear.
The teacher then repeats this procedure with several other intervals.

MELODY PLAYBACK

The teacher selects one of the following melodies, names the key, plays the tonic chord ONCE,
and then plays the melody TWICE. The student then plays back the melody from memory.

For additional material, see the series *Melody Playback/Singback* and *Rhythm Clapback/Singback*.

★ FOUR STAR TEST NO. 10 ★

GIVEN BY THE TEACHER AT THE LESSON

SIGHT-READING TEST

Teacher's grading

Play with the given fingering.

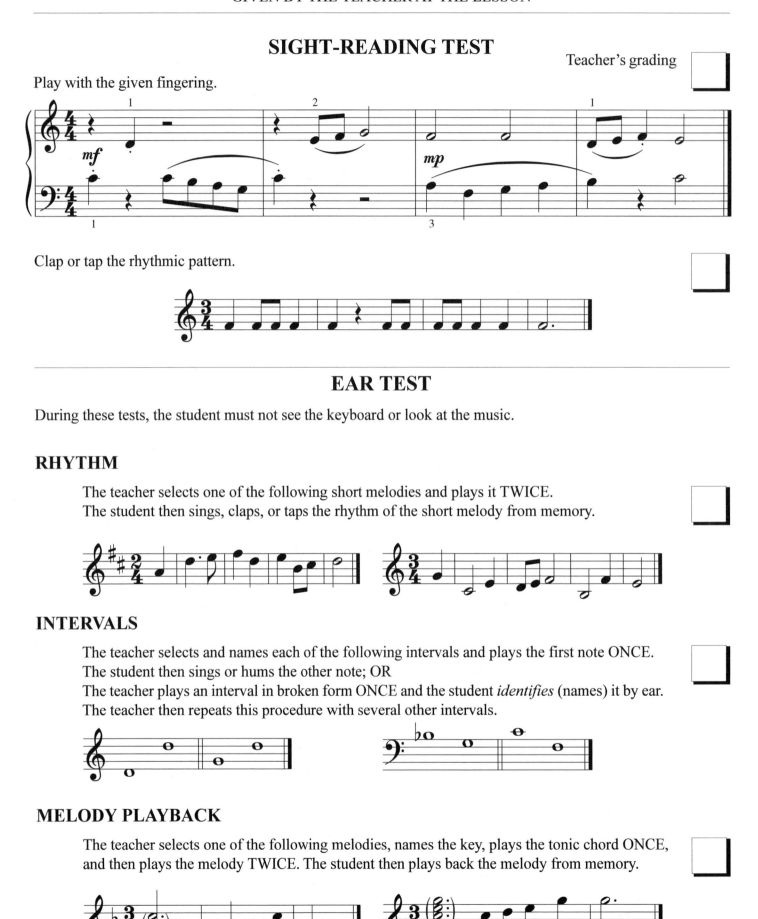

Clap or tap the rhythmic pattern.

EAR TEST

During these tests, the student must not see the keyboard or look at the music.

RHYTHM

The teacher selects one of the following short melodies and plays it TWICE.
The student then sings, claps, or taps the rhythm of the short melody from memory.

INTERVALS

The teacher selects and names each of the following intervals and plays the first note ONCE.
The student then sings or hums the other note; OR
The teacher plays an interval in broken form ONCE and the student *identifies* (names) it by ear.
The teacher then repeats this procedure with several other intervals.

MELODY PLAYBACK

The teacher selects one of the following melodies, names the key, plays the tonic chord ONCE, and then plays the melody TWICE. The student then plays back the melody from memory.

For additional material, see the series *Melody Playback/Singback* and *Rhythm Clapback/Singback*.

★ FINAL FOUR STAR TEST ★

This test will be given before filling in and signing the Certificate of Achievement.

SIGHT-READING TEST

Teacher's grading

Play with the given fingering.

Clap or tap the rhythmic patterns.

EAR TEST

During these tests, the student must not see the keyboard or look at the music.

RHYTHM

The teacher selects one of the following short melodies and plays it TWICE.
The student then sings, claps, or taps the rhythm of the short melody from memory.

INTERVALS

The teacher selects and names each of the following intervals and plays the first note ONCE.
The student then sings or hums the other note; OR
The teacher plays an interval in broken form ONCE and the student *identifies* (names) it by ear.
The teacher then repeats this procedure with several other intervals.

MELODY PLAYBACK

The teacher selects one of the following melodies, names the key, plays the tonic chord ONCE, and then plays the melody TWICE. The student then plays back the melody from memory.

For additional material, see the series *Melody Playback/Singback* and *Rhythm Clapback/Singback*.